Usborne
First Wipe-Clean
Big Letters

Illustrated by Ailie Busby

Written by
Jessica Greenwell

round
letters

straight and
round letters

S O

U J

Q

B D

C G

P R

Designed by
Matt Durber and Stephanie Jeffries

Start at the big dot.

T

Trace over the letters on Turtle and Tiger, and on the trees and the towel, too.

Trace over this letter and write some more, if you want to.

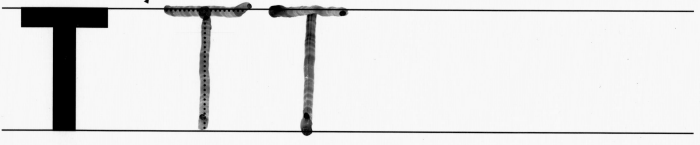

Trace over the letters on the ice creams and the ice-cream stand.

Start at the big dot.

I like ice cream.

Start at the big dot.

Trace over the letters on the happy horses...

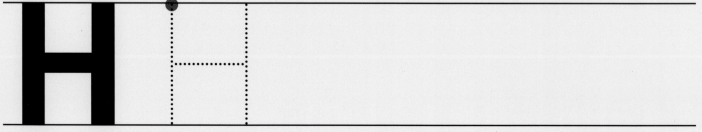

...and on the leaping llamas.

Start at the big dot.

Start at the big dot.

F lamingos

Flap

Flap

Trace over the letters on the four flapping flamingos.

Elephants

Start at the big dot.

E

Excuse me!

Trace over each letter on the elephants' ears.

E

Start at the big dot.

Trace over the letters on the acrobatic alligators.

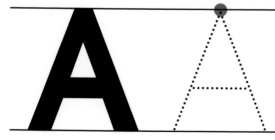

V v

Start at the big dot.

Trace over the letters on the van...

Weeee!

...and in the water.

Start at the big dot.

W w

Start at the big dot.

Trace over the
letters on the yaks.

Start at the big dot.

K

1   2

Trace over
the letters on
the kangaroos'
kayaks.

K   k

Start at the big dot.

Trace over the letters on the monkeys.

Mmmm

Trace over the letters on the narwhals.

Start at the big dot.

Nice to meet you.

Start at the big dot.

Trace over the letters in this exciting picture.

X marks the spot!

Trace over the letters on the zebras.

Start at the big dot.

Trace over the letters on the seahorses, snail and starfish.

Snails have swirly shells.

O

Start at the big dot.

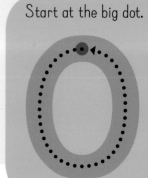

Trace over the letters on the ostrich and the oval eggs.

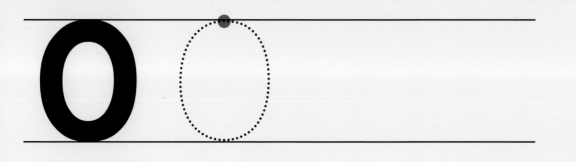

Quack!

Quiet!

Start at the big dot.

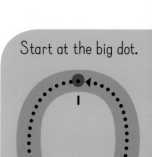

Trace over the letters on the quacking ducks.

Q

Start at the big dot.

Trace over the letters
on the chameleons.

C

chameleons
have curly
tails.

C c

Trace over the letters on the giraffes.

Start at the big dot.

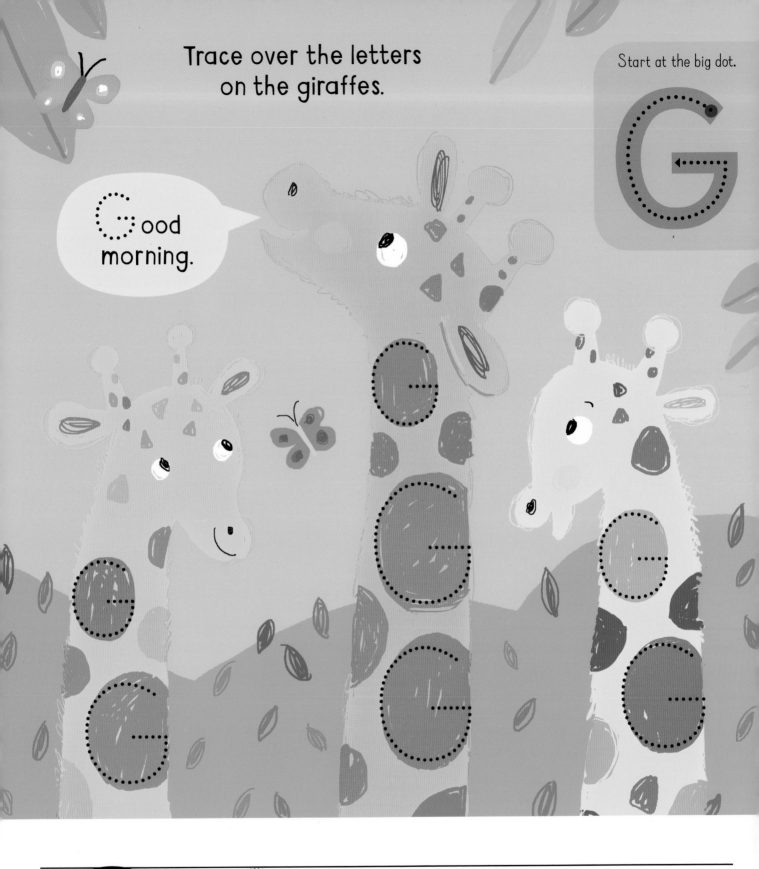

Good morning.

U

Trace over the letters on the umbrellas.

U

Trace over the
letters on the
jaguars' jet packs.

Start at the big dot.

J

Start at the big dot.

Trace over the birds
on their branches.

Beautiful!

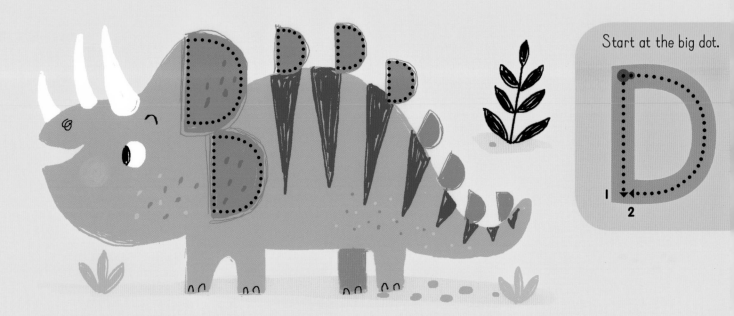

Start at the big dot.

Trace over the letters on the dinosaurs.

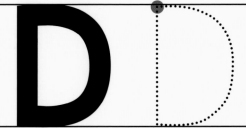

P

2 ◄—
↓
1

Trace over the letters on the plodding penguins.

P P